LITTLE BOOK
❖ OF ❖
RABBITS

WEIDENFELD & NICOLSON
LONDON

The Private Life
of the Rabbit

The rabbit is a vegetarian, timid, retiring. It may raid the vegetable plot, but it does not attack man or man's domestic animals. Its little excursions to nibble carrots, lettuces, peas, are tiresome, but, like the misbehaviour of children whom we nevertheless love, can be corrected by our watchfulness. Like children, the rabbits in garden, field and hutch endear themselves to us by their innocent, happy preoccupation with their simple way of living. Small wonder that in the traditional nursery tales the rabbit is both the *enfant terrible* and the lovable creature. Beatrix Potter and a hundred other authors have created the acceptable image of careless, cheerful, clever Rabbit...Uncle Remus's Br'er Rabbit always wins in the battle of wits with Br'er Fox.

from THE PRIVATE LIFE OF THE RABBIT
R. M. Lockley

Bunny Rabbit

*B*unny creeps out and caresses his nose,
Combs out his ears with his fluttering toes,
       Blinks at the sun
       And commences to run
       With a skip and a hop
       And a flippety-flop,
Nibbling the clover wherever he goes;
But only when he is quite easy in mind
Does he button his little white tail down behind.

*B*unny stops dead and stiffens each hair,
And his eyelids freeze in a terrified stare,
       And he pricks up his ears,
       For the sound that he hears
       Is a low muffled beat
       And a drumming of feet
And an ominous rub-a-dub-dubbing –
  but where?
He's off like the wind! He's off like the wind!
And his little white tail unbuttoned behind.

BUNNY RABBIT
Anonymous

SCREEN OF RABBITS AND GRASSES

Kano School mid-15th century

RABBITS

FLOPSY BUNNIES

>—<

When Benjamin Bunny grew up, he married his Cousin Flopsy. They had a large family, and they were very improvident and cheerful.

I do not remember the separate names of their children; they were generally called the 'Flopsy Bunnies'.

from THE TALE OF
THE FLOPSY BUNNIES
Beatrix Potter 1866–1943

7

RABBITS
Henry Weekes fl.1849–1888

RABBIT HABBIT

There was an Old Person whose habits,
Induced him to feed upon Rabbits,
When he'd eaten eighteen,
He turned perfectly green,
Upon which he relinquished those habits.

Edward Lear 1812–1888

RABBITS

RABBITS·AND STRAWBERRIES *Anonymous*

RABBITS

Little Rabbit Sprig

There was a little Rabbit sprig,
Which being little was not big;
He always walked upon his feet,
And never fasted when he eat.
When from a place he did run away,
He never at that place did stay;
And when he ran, as I am told,
He ne'er stood still for young or old
Tho' ne'er instructed by a cat,
He knew a mouse was not a rat:
One day, as I am certified,
He took a whim and fairly died:
And, as I'm told, by men of sense,
He never has been walking since.

A LITTLE RABBIT
Anonymous

RABBITS

RABBIT BURROWS

Another temptation to idleness and sporting, was a number of rabbits, which possessed all the hillocks and dry places: but these being inconvenient to the huntsmen, on account of their burrows, when they came to take away the deer, they permitted the country-people to destroy them all.

from THE NATURAL HISTORY
OF SELBORNE
Gilbert White 1720–1793

RABBITS

QUEEN MARY'S PSALTER
early 14th century

GOOD FRIENDS
Alfred Barber fl.1879–1893

RABBITS

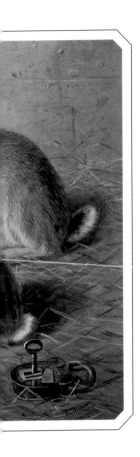

Sir Bunny

Sir Bunny is a splendid shot,
   And every time he fires,
   A farmer or a keeper falls,
Sometimes a brace of squires.

He went out shooting yesterday
   With young Lord Leveret;
But the wind it blew, and the
      rain it pour'd
   And both got soaking wet.

SIR BUNNY
Traditional

15

A LITTLE RABBIT

A little rabbit on a hill
Was bobbing up and down;
His tail was soft and white,
His two long ears were brown.
But when he heard a roaring noise
Made by the farmer's van,
His tiny whiskers trembled
And down his hole he ran.

A LITTLE RABBIT
Traditional

RABBIT

Sue Warner

DISCOVERED
Helena Maguire 1860–1909

RABBITS

RABBIT WARRENS

Nearly all the warrens have an *Owsla*, or a group of strong or clever rabbits – second year or older – surrounding the Chief Rabbit and his doe and exercising authority. Owslas vary. In one warren, the Owsla may be the band of a war-lord: in another, it may consist largely of clever patrollers or garden-raiders. Sometimes a good story-teller may find a place; or a seer, or intuitive rabbit.

from WATERSHIP DOWN
Richard Adams

RABBITS

Who'll Help a Fairy?

'Oh! what shall I do?' sobbed a tiny mole,
'A Fairy has tumbled into my hole;
It is full of water and crawling things,
And she can't get out, for she's hurt her wings.

'I did my best to catch hold her hair,
But my arms are short, and she's still in there.
Oh! help her, white rabbit, your arms are long;
You say you're good, and I know you're strong.'

'Don't bother me,' the white rabbit said –
She shut up her eyes, and her ears grew red –
'There's lots of mud, and it's sure to stick
On my beautiful fur, so white and thick.'

'Oh dear! oh dear!' sobbed the poor little mole,
'Who'll help the Fairy out of the hole?'
A little brown rabbit popped up from the gorse,
'I'm not very strong but I'll try, of course.'

RABBITS

A RABBIT AMONG THE FAIRIES
John Anster Fitzgerald 1832-1906

His little tail bobbed as he waddled in,
The muddy water came up to his chin;
But he caught the Fairy tight by the hand,
And helped her to get to Fairyland.

But she kissed him first on his muddy nose,
She kissed his face and his little wet toes;
And when the day dawned in the early light,
The common brown rabbit was silvery white.

WHO'LL HELP A FAIRY?
Anonymous

21

RABBITS

RABBITS LITHOGRAPH

from Études D'Animaux D'Après Nature 1854

22

Disgraceful

The rabbit has a charming face:
Its private life is a disgrace.
I really dare not name to you
The awful things that rabbits do;
Things that your paper never prints –
You only mention them in hints.
They have such lost, degraded souls
No wonder they inhabit holes;
When such depravity is found
It only can live underground.

THE RABBIT
Anonymous

THE SNARE

I hear a sudden cry of pain!
  There is a rabbit in a snare;
Now I hear the cry again,
  But I cannot tell from where.

But I cannot tell from where
  He is calling out for aid;
Crying on the frightened air,
  Making everything afraid.

Making everything afraid,
  Wrinkling up his little face,
As he cries again for aid;
  And I cannot find the place!

And I cannot find the place
  Where his paw is in the snare;
Little one! Oh, little one!
  I am searching everywhere.

THE SNARE
James Stephens 1882–1950

RABBITS

THE PET BUNNY
James Thomas Watts 1853–1930

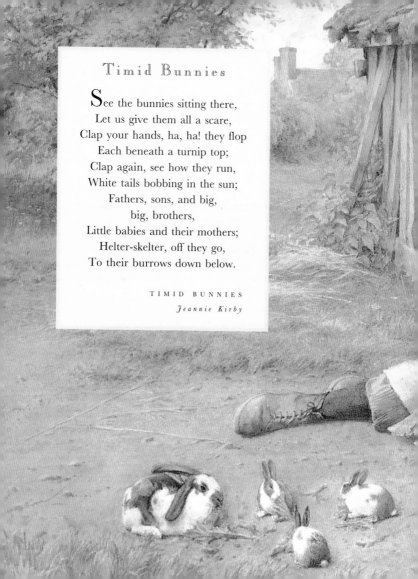

Timid Bunnies

See the bunnies sitting there,
Let us give them all a scare,
Clap your hands, ha, ha! they flop
Each beneath a turnip top;
Clap again, see how they run,
White tails bobbing in the sun;
Fathers, sons, and big,
            big, brothers,
Little babies and their mothers;
Helter-skelter, off they go,
To their burrows down below.

TIMID BUNNIES
Jeannie Kirby

THE FARMER'S BOY
Charles Edward Wilson 1891–1936

PREDATOR AND PREY

❧ ❧

T he rabbit froze, held his gaze,
Watched the hawk, knew his ways,
Two ancient enemies, predator and prey,
He'll live to see another day.

ANCIENT ENEMIES
Isaac Stewart

SCREEN OF RABBITS
AND GRASSES
Kano School mid-15th century

RABBITS

PLAYING GAMES
Macwhirter

HIDDEN LAIR

The birds are gone to bed the cows are still
And sheep lie panting on each old mole hill
And underneath the willows grey-green bough
Like toil a resting – lies the fallow plough
The timid hares throw daylight fears away
On the lanes road to dust and dance and play
The dabble in the grain by nought deterred
To lick the dewfall from the barleys beard
Then out they sturt again and round the hill
Like happy thoughts dance squat and loiter still
Till milking maidens in the early morn
Gingle their yokes and start them in the corn
Through well known beaten paths each nimbling hare
Sturts quick as fear – and seeks its hidden lair.

HARES AT PLAY

RABBITS

MASTER RABBIT

⤜⤛

As I was walking,
Thyme sweet to my nose,
Green grasshoppers talking,
Rose rivalling rose:

Wings clear as amber,
Outspread in the light,
As from bush to bush
The Linnet took flight:

Master Rabbit I saw
In the shadow-rimmed mouth
Of his sandy cavern
Looking out to the South,

'Twas dew-tide coming,
The turf was sweet
To nostril, curved tooth,
And wool-soft feet.

Sun was in West,
Crystal in beam
Of its golden shower
Did his round eye gleam.

Lank horror was I,
And a foe, poor soul –
Snowy flit of a scut,
He was into his hole:

And – stamp, stamp, stamp
Through the dim labyrinths
  clear –
The whole world darkened:
A Human was near!

MASTER RABBIT
Walter de la Mare 1873-1956

A DOE RABBIT AND
HER TWO YOUNG
John Frederick Herring Snr
1795–1865

33

ALICE IN WONDERLAND
Frederick Morgan 1856–1927

RABBITS

The White Rabbit

He is white as Helvellyn when winter is well in;
  His whiskers are mobile and tender.
If it weren't for the greed that compels him to feed
  Without ceasing, his form would be slender.

With elegant hops he crushes or crops
  All the flowers that bloom in the garden;
Yet such is the grace that suffuses his face,
  He wins, without asking, our pardon.

The sun, who rides heaven from Dover to Devon
  Inspecting furred folk and their habits,
Breaks out into poesy: 'What summer snow is he
  Made of, this pearl among rabbits?'

And at night on the lawn as he waits for the dawn,
  Rapt in dreams of a rabbit's perfection,
The moon in her stride sweeps the cloudlets aside
  To rejoice in his silver reflection.

THE WHITE RABBIT
E. V. Rieu

RABBITS

OLD TINEY

*H*ere lies, whom hound did ne'er pursue,
Nor swifter greyhound follow,
Whose feet ne'er tainted morning dew,
Nor ear heard huntsmen's hallo'.

Old Tiney, surliest of his kind,
Who, nurs'd with tender care,
And to domestic bounds confin'd,
Was still a wild Jack-hare.

Though duly from my hand he took
His pittance ev'ry night,
He did it with a jealous look,
And, when he could, would bite.

EPITAPH ON A HARE
William Cowper 1731–1800

FEEDING BUNNY
Mark W. Langlois fl.1862–1873

Brown Bunny

Brown bunny sits inside his burrow
  Till everything is still,
Then out he slips along the furrow,
  Or up the grassy hill.

He nibbles all about the bushes
  Or sits to wash his face,
But at a sound he stamps, and rushes
  At a surprising pace.

You see some little streaks and flashes,
  A last sharp twink of white,
As down his hidey-hole he dashes
  And disappears from sight.

THE RABBIT
Edith King

THE RABBIT WARREN
George Marks 1880–1939

RABBITS

BIG EYES

When they said the time to hide was mine,
I hid back under a thick grape vine.

And while I was still for the time to pass,
A little gray thing came out of the grass.

He hopped his way through the melon bed
And sat down close by a cabbage head.

He sat down close where I could see,
And his big still eyes looked hard at me,

His big eyes bursting out of the rim,
And I looked back very hard at him.

THE RABBIT
Elizabeth Madox Roberts 1886–1940

AFTER WORK

Walter Hunt 1861–1941

RABBITS

Dancing Rabbits

*W*e who play under the pines,
  We who dance in the snow
That shines blue in the light of the moon
  Sometimes halt as we go,
Stand with our ears erect,
  Our noses testing the air,
To gaze at the golden world
  Behind the window there.

RABBITS

Suns they have in a cave
   And stars each on a tall white stem,
And the thought of fox or night owl
   Seems never to trouble them,
They laugh and they eat and are warm,
   Their food seems ready at hand,
While hungry out in the cold
   We little rabbits stand.

But they never dance as we dance,
   They have not the speed nor the grace.
We scorn both the cat and the dog
   Who lie by their fireplace.
We scorn them licking their paws,
   Their eyes on an upraised spoon,
We who dance hungry and wild
   Under a winter's moon.

SONGS OF THE RABBITS
OUTSIDE THE TAVERN
Elizabeth Coatsworth

RABBITS AND GRASSES
Kano School mid-15th century

RABBITS

RABBIT BE CAREFUL

Couch among the heather
Never mind the weather,
Forget it altogether,
Run from a dog, a man, a gun,
Or your happy young life will
    soon be undone.

from TIM RABBIT
Alison Uttley 1884–1976

RABBITS

FURRY COMPANIONS

Emily Mary Osborn b.1834

RABBITS

LOP-EARED RABBITS AND A TERRIER

Horatio Henry Couldery fl. 1832–1893

PRINCE OF RABBITS

What Robin Hood is to the English and John Henry to the American Negroes, Elil-Hrair-Rah, or El-ahrairah – The Prince with a Thousand Enemies – is to rabbits. Uncle Remus might well have heard of him, for some of El-ahrairah's adventures are those of Brer Rabbit. For that matter, Odysseus himself might have borrowed a trick or two from the rabbit hero, for he is very old and was never at a loss for a trick to deceive his enemies...Some rabbits say he controls the weather, because the wind, the damp and the dew are friends and instruments to rabbits against their enemies.

from WATERSHIP DOWN
Richard Adams

RABBITS

Alice's Adventures

›‹

Alice was beginning to get very tired of sitting by her sister on the bank…when suddenly a White Rabbit with pink eyes ran close by her.

There was nothing so *very* remarkable in that; nor did Alice think it so *very* much out of the way to hear the Rabbit say to itself, 'Oh dear! Oh dear! I shall be too late!'…but when the Rabbit actually *took a watch out of its waistcoat-pocket,* and looked at it, and then hurried on, Alice started to her feet, for it flashed across her mind that she had never before seen a rabbit with either a waistcoat-pocket or a watch to take out of it, and burning with curiosity, she ran across the field after it, and fortunately was just in time to see it pop down a large rabbit-hole under the hedge.

from ALICE'S ADVENTURES
IN WONDERLAND
Lewis Carroll 1832–1898

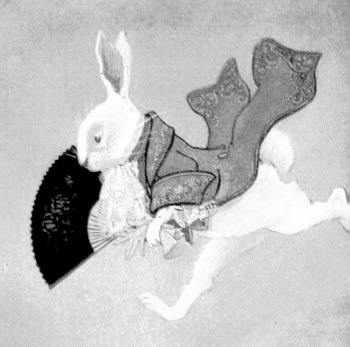

*from Alice's Adventures
in Wonderland
Gwynedd M. Hudson*

Gwynedd M.Hudson.

RABBITS

RABBITS

RABBIT AND LARK

'Under the ground
  It's rumbly and dark
And interesting,'
  Said Rabbit to Lark.

Said Lark to Rabbit,
  'Up in the sky
There's plenty of room
  And it's airy and high.'

'Under the ground
  It's warm and dry.
Won't you live with me?'
  Was Rabbit's reply.

'The air's so sunny.
  I wish you'd agree,'
Said the little Lark,
  'To live with me.'

But under the ground
  And up in the sky,
Larks can't burrow
  Nor rabbits fly.

So Skylark over
  And Rabbit under
They had to settle
  To live asunder.

And often these two friends
  Meet with a will
For a chat together
  On the top of the hill.

RABBIT AND LARK
James Reeves

51

On the Alert

W'en ole man Rabbit say 'scoot', dey scooted, en w'en ole Miss Rabbit say 'scat', dey scatted.

UNCLE REMUS:
PLANTATION PROVERBS
Joel Chander Harris (1848–1908)

I'M COMING AFTER YOU

B. Cobbe

THE PET RABBIT
Alfred Tidey 1806–1892

Equal Grace

*W*ho believes that equal grace
God extends in every place,
Little difference he scans
'Twixt a rabbit's God and man's.

BATTLE BUNNY
Francis Brett Harte 1836–1902

RABBITS

Acknowledgements

Copyright © Weidenfeld and Nicolson 1996
First published in Great Britain in 1996 by
George Weidenfeld and Nicolson Ltd
Orion House, 5 Upper St Martin's Lane,
London WC2H 9EA

British Library Cataloguing in Publication Data.
A catalogue record for this book is available
from the British Library.

Designed and created by
THE BRIDGEWATER BOOK COMPANY
Words chosen by JOANNE JESSOP
Picture research by FELICITY COX *and*
VANESSA FLETCHER
Page make-up by JANE LANAWAY
Printed in Italy

*The publishers wish to thank the following for
the use of pictures:*
BRIDGEMAN ART LIBRARY: p.17; Bonhams p.22;
British Library pp.5, 13, 29, 42; Chris Beetles
pp.38–9; Philips Fine Art pp.33, 50. FINE ART
PHOTOGRAPHIC LIBRARY: front and back covers,
title page, pp.8–9, 10–11, 18, 21, 25, 26–7, 34,
37, 46, 53, 54; courtesy of Anthony Mitchell,
Nottingham pp.14–15; Burlington Paintings
p.2; Caelt Gallery p.30; Haynes Fine Art
pp.40–1; Stephanie Knight Library p.45.
Reproduced by permission of FREDERICK
WARNE & CO.: p.6 (Copyright© Frederick
Warne & Co., 1909, 1987).

*The publishers gratefully acknowledge permission
to reproduce the following material in this book:*
p.3 *Private Life of the Rabbit* (1967) by R.M.
Lockley; by permission of Andre Deutsch Ltd.
p. 7 *The Tale of the Flopsy Bunnies* by Beatrix
Potter © F Warne & Co., 1909; by permission
of Frederick Warne and Co. pp. 19 and 47
Watership Down by Richard Adams published by
Penguin Books. p. 24 *The Snare* by James
Stephens by permission of the Society of
Authors as the literary representatives of the
Estate of James Stephens. p. 28 *Ancient Enemies*
by permission of the author. p. 32 *Master Rabbit*
by Walter de la Mare by permission of the
Literary Trustees of Walter de la Mare, and the
Society of Authors as their representative. p. 35
The White Rabbit by E.V. Rieu from *A Puffin
Quartet of Poets* © 1958; by permission of
Penguin Books. p. 40 *The Rabbit* by Elizabeth
Madox Roberts from *Under the Tree* © Viking
Kestrel; by permission of Penguin Books. p. 44
Tim Rabbit from *The Adventures of No Ordinary
Rabbit* by Alison Uttley; by permission of Faber
and Faber Ltd. p. 51 *Rabbit and Lark* by James
Reaves from *A Puffin Quartet of Poets* © 1958; by
permission of Penguin Books.

*Every effort has been made to trace
all copyright holders and obtain
permissions. The editor and publishers
sincerely apologise for any inadvertent
errors or omissions and will be happy
to correct them in any future edition.*